D1272615

TED McKEEVER'S
METROPŌL

METROPOL
Volume 2
Copyright © 2001 Ted McKeever. All Right Reserved.
All characters featured in this issue, the distinct likenesses thereof,
and all related inditia are trademarks of Ted McKeever.

Grateful thanks to Hans Rueffert at Luna7.
Visit Metropol on the web:
www.luna7.com/metropol

Published by
SORHENN GRAFIKS
Info@sorhenngrafiks.com

Printed by
Quebecor Lebonfon
Canada

ISBN : 2-914406-04-5

CHAPTER FOUR

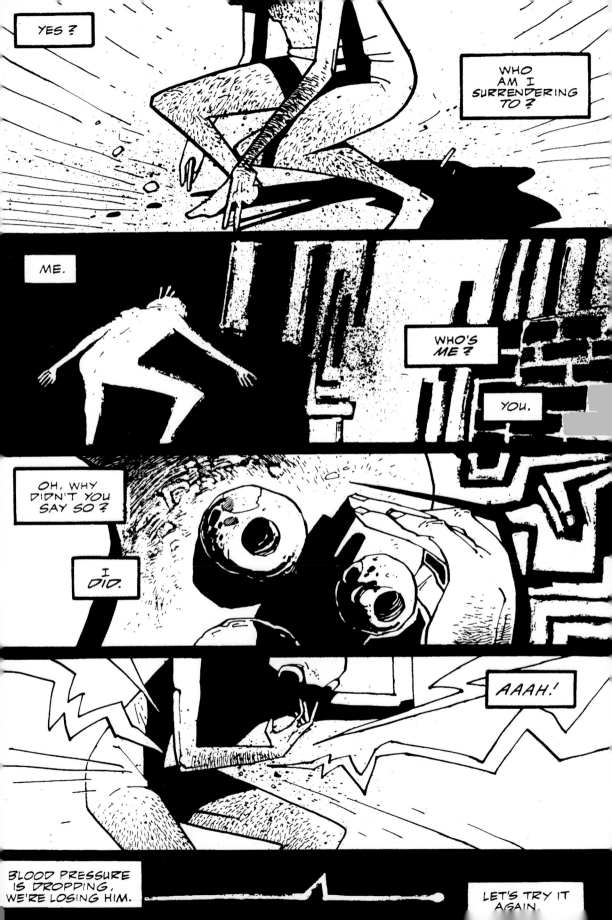

The BREATH of REPTILES

NEXT: NO ONE MOVE A MUSCLE AS THE DEAD COME HOME. (Part 1 of 2)

CHAPTER FIVE

...WE'VE JUST RECEIVED WORD THAT GROUPS OF "MONSTERS" ARE BEING SIGHTED AT VARIOUS PARTS OF THE *WEST* AND *NORTH* SIDES OF THE CITY.

THOUGH THESE REPORTS ARE *UNCONFIRMED* BY POLICE, *ENOUGH* OF THESE SIGHTINGS HAVE BEEN RECEIVED TO MAKE THIS *MORE* THAN AN ISOLATED INCIDENT.

THOUGH WE *HESITATE* TO USE THE WORD *"MONSTER"*, IT IS THE DESCRIPTION GIVEN BY WITNESSES, SO WE WILL ADHERE TO THEIR *"DEFINITION"*, IF ONLY TO *ACCURATELY* PORTRAY THEIR *IMPRESSION.*

WHETHER THESE SIGHTINGS HAVE *ANYTHING* TO DO WITH THE *RECENT* OUTBREAK OF AN APPARENT *PLAGUE*, IS UNKNOWN AT THIS TIME.

WHAT WE *DO* KNOW IS THAT THE *PLAGUE* IS MUCH MORE *WIDE-SPREAD* THAN ORIGINALLY REPORTED.

WE HAVE JUST BEEN INFORMED THAT THE NUMBER OF PLAGUE VICTIMS HAS RISEN TO *OVER THREE THOUSAND.* DUE TO RECENT EVENTS, WE ARE ADVISING EVERYONE TO *STAY IN THEIR HOMES,* AND TO AWAIT WORD ON PROPER PROCEDURES. WE ARE *UNCONDITIONALLY* ADMINISTERING A STATE OF *EMERGENCY,* AND ARE ASKING, UNLESS *EXTREMELY NECESSARY,* THAT YOU *STAY IN YOUR HOMES,* AND AWAIT FURTHER INSTRUCTIONS.
I HAVE JUST BEEN HANDED THIS REPORT. *OH, COME ON...* YOU DON'T EXPECT ME TO ... *BUT...* THERE HAS *APPARENTLY* BEEN A SIGHTING OF ... *ARE WE SURE ABOUT THIS?* I MEAN *MONSTERS,* OKAY, THERE'S SOME BELIEVABILITY, BUT *THIS?*

OKAY, *OKAY!* WE'VE JUST RE- CEIVED WORD THAT SEVERAL PEOPLE ON THE EAST SIDE OF THE CITY HAVE REPORTED SEE- ING ... AN ANGEL. YES, AN ANGEL. THAT'S WHAT IT SAYS, RIGHT HERE THEY STATED THAT IT WAS "HOVER- ING" OUTSIDE, ABOUT FOUR STORIES UP, IN THE *MIDDLE* OF THE STREET. AND THAT AT ONE POINT THE "ANGEL" *APPARENTLY* FIRED A GUN TOWARDS ... FIRED A GUN? SINCE WHEN DID ANGEL START CARRYING GUNS?

SINCE NOW.

DEJA VU.

NEXT:

THE ONLY THING THAT SHINES. PART TWO OF TWO

CHAPTER SIX

IN VIEW OF THE RECENT *EXTRAORDINARY* EVENTS, NO ONE CAN SAY FOR SURE THAT THEY WERE FORESEEABLE.

IN FACT, EVEN AT *THIS* STAGE, WHAT IS TO COME IS *DENIABLE*.

APPARENT *"MONSTERS"* ROAM THE STREETS, *THOUSANDS* ARE DYING EACH DAY FROM THE *PLAGUE*, NOT TO MENTION THE NUMEROUS REPORTS OF *ASSAULTS*.

WE'VE HAD EVERYTHING FROM PEOPLE WITH *"BUFFALO HEADS"* TO *"ANGELS WITH GUNS"*.

WHAT WOULD NO DOUBT MAKE *ONE-HELL-OF-A* NIGHTMARE, IS NOW A *REALITY*.

THE *BIRTH RATE* HAS NOW BEEN OVERTAKEN BY THE *DEATH RATE*.

BIRTH CONTROL IS NO LONGER A CONCERN.

DEATH CONTROL HAS BEGUN TO DEFINE ITSELF.

A STABLE *BALANCE* BETWEEN HUMAN NUMBERS LIVING AND THOSE DYING, OR DEAD, HAS BEEN *DRASTICALLY* ALTERED.

IT IS NOW *OBVIOUS* THAT THE REMAINING PEOPLE OF THIS CITY ARE ON COURSE FOR ONE OF THE MOST *MASSIVE* AND *EXTRAORDINARY ECOLOGICAL UPHEAVALS* THEY HAVE EVER KNOWN.

IN AN EFFORT TO UNDERSTAND WHAT LIES *AHEAD*, WE MUST FIRST UNDERSTAND WHAT WE LEAVE *BEHIND*.

KNOWLEDGE.

ACTUALITY.

AND ORGANIZATION...

...ARE NO LONGER *VALID*.

ALREADY THE CITY IS OVERRUN WITH VIOLENCE AND MAYHEM, ABOUNDING AT SUCH A RATE TOO OVERWHELMING TO HUMANLY ENDURE.

NEW RULES WILL BE NEEDED.

NEW LEADERS WILL BE *IMPERATIVE*.

WE ARE *ALREADY* CAPABLE OF MAINTAINING OURSELVES FROM WITHIN, THOUGH I WOULD VENTURE TO BELIEVE THAT THOUGH IT WAS ONCE A *"PREFERENCE"*, IT WILL NOW BECOME *COMPULSORY.*

A WALL OF *MASSIVE PROPORTIONS* IS BEING CONSTRUCTED ON THE OUTSKIRTS OF THE CITY AT THIS *VERY MOMENT.*

THOUGH I DON'T KNOW *ALL* THE DETAILS, I WOULD VENTURE A GUESS THAT THEY INTEND TO SEAL OFF THE *"INFECTED AREA"* AND NOT ALLOW THE PLAGUE TO SPREAD.

  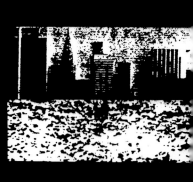

... LOCATIONS.

THE PICTURES YOU ARE SEEING WERE TAKEN EARLIER TODAY, JUST AFTER WE LEARNED OF IT'S CONSTRUCTION. AND FROM THE LOOKS OF HOW MUCH THEY'VE COMPLETED, I'D SAY THAT THEY'VE *KNOWN* OF THIS FOR *QUITE SOME TIME.*

I'VE ALSO RECENTLY BEEN INFORMED THAT ALL TRAFFIC, BOTH *ENTERING* AND *EXITING* THE CITY'S LIMITS, HAS BEEN *HALTED...*

... AND ANYONE TRYING TO PASS THESE BORDERS WILL BE *EXECUTED ON SIGHT.*

I THINK IT'S *SAFE TO SAY* THAT THEY HAVE NO INTENTION OF *CURING,* OR *REVERSING,* WHAT IS *ALREADY* IN MOTION. NOT TO SAY THAT THEY COULD EVEN IF THEY WANTED TO

... IT'S JUST THAT IF THEY CAN CONTAIN THE PLAGUE HERE *BEFORE* IT SPREADS, WE CAN AT LEAST HAVE *CONSOLATION* IN OUR OWN *MARTYRDOM.*

AND IF THERE IS *ANY* SATISFACTION, IT'S KNOWING THAT THE *POWERS* THAT HAVE CHOSEN THIS *"ISOLATION"* HAVE DONE SO WITH THE *INCLUSION* OF *THEMSELVES.*

HAVING NOT HAD *RELATIONS* WITH ANY OUTSIDE PUBLIC FOR *YEARS,* IT IS UNLIKELY THAT THEY WOULD COME TO OUR AID *NOW...*

...NOR WOULD WE *ASK* FOR IT.

WE STILL HAVE SOME DIG...

HEY, WHO SWITCHED CAMERAS?

PAM, WAS THAT *YOU?* YOU HIT THE WRONG BUTTON?

HEY, ARE YOU DEAF?

TV 5 NEWSWATCH

YOU'RE NOT SUPPOSED TO BE AT *THAT* CAMERA.

I KNOW
YOU'RE THE
ONLY ONE
ON THE
FLOOR, BUT
DAGNAMIT...

OH...I'M
SORRY.

I HAVEN'T...
SORRY PAM.
HAVEN'T HAD
MUCH SLEEP
THESE DAYS.
THAT'S FINE,
PAM.

THIS MAY BE THE
LAST VESTIGE OF IN-
FORMATION THAT *YOU*
RECEIVE FOR QUITE
SOME TIME. SO, RATHER
THAN WASTE IT ON *RAM-
BLINGS* THAT NO LONGER
HAVE ANY VALUE, LET ME
TAKE WHAT TIME *REMAINS*
AND RECITE A VERSE I
FEEL IS APPROPRIATE IN
THE FACE OF THE
COMING *APOCALYPSE.*

" I STAND ON
THE SIDE OF THE WEST
OF THE CITY FOUR-
SQUARE. AND I FACE
THE EAST AND THE
KINGS AND QUEENS
OF THE EAST TO
GATHER THEM TO
THE BATTLE OF THAT
GREAT DAY OF GOD
ALMIGHTY.

" I RAISE MY HANDS
FOR THE RELEASE OF THE
MOMENTUM OF THE VIOLET
FLAME THAT SHALL RE-
VERSE THE TIDE OF DARK-
NESS AND ROLL IT BACK
FROM THE WEST ONTO
THE EAST. AND IT SHALL
BE AS THE ROLLING-UP
OF A MIGHTY SCROLL. AND
IT SHALL BE THE ROLLING-UP
OF THAT DARKNESS WHICH
HAS COVERED THE LAND.

"AND IT SHALL BE THE
ROLLING UP OF UNCLEAN
SPIRITS THAT, LIKE FROGS,
HAVE BEEN SENT FORTH
OUT OF THE MOUTH OF
THE DRAGON AND OUT
OF THE MOUTH OF
THE BEAST AND OUT
OF THE MOUTH OF THE
FALSE ..." HUH?

TCHICK!

TTSSSSSSSHHHHHHHHH!

AS FOR THE REST, WELL, T IS ... *UNIQUE.* BUT, I REALLY *CAN'T* SAY THAT I *DON'T* LIKE IT.

IT HAS A CERTAIN SENSE OF ...

HEY, WHAT'S GOIN' ON?

BLACKOUT, ENOCH.

I WAS WONDERING HOW *LONG* IT WOULD TAKE FOR THEM TO TAKE CONTROL.

"THE *DEMONS?*"

"YEAH. THEY'RE MOVING *QUICKER* THAN I ANTICIPATED. *NO DOUBT* THE BLACKOUT IS SPREADING ACROSS THE CITY AS WE SPEAK. THAT'S WHY WE DIDN'T SEE ANY MORE OF THEM AFTER THE INCIDENT AT THE *DRUGSTORE.* BUT THAT'S *FINE,* THE DARKNESS WORKS FOR *US* AS MUCH AS IT DOES FOR *THEM...*"

"...THEY NO DOUBT PLAN ON *RECRUITING* AS MANY MEMBERS TO THEIR *SIDE* BEFORE WE CAN UNIFY OURS."

"WHAT *DO* WE NEED TO *DO?*"

"WELL, SITTIN' HERE ISN'T GETTIN' US ANYWHERE. LET'S GET OUTSIDE AND TRY TO GET TO *HIGHER GROUND.*"

"HOW ABOUT HEADIN' TOWARDS THE *POWER*

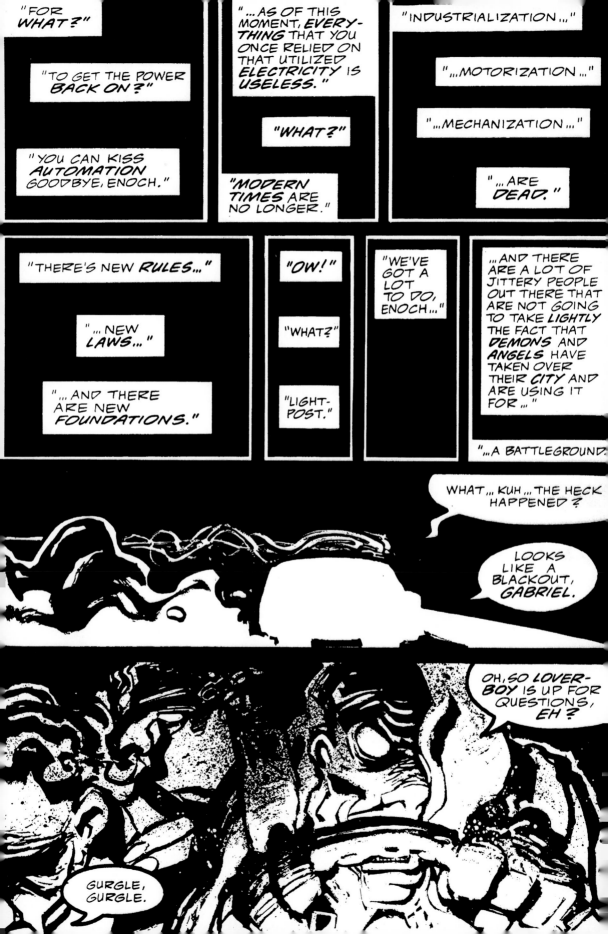

NEXT:

EVIL IS AN EXACT SCIENCE.